DESTRUCTION DERBY

by Anabel Dean
Teacher
Redding, California

BENEFIC PRESS
Westchester, Illinois

RACING WHEELS SERIES

Hot Rod

Destruction Derby

Drag Race

Stock Car Race

Road Race

Indy 500

Library of Congress
Number 78-170771

Copyright 1972 by Benefic Press
All Rights Reserved
Printed in the United States of America

CONTENTS

Chapter

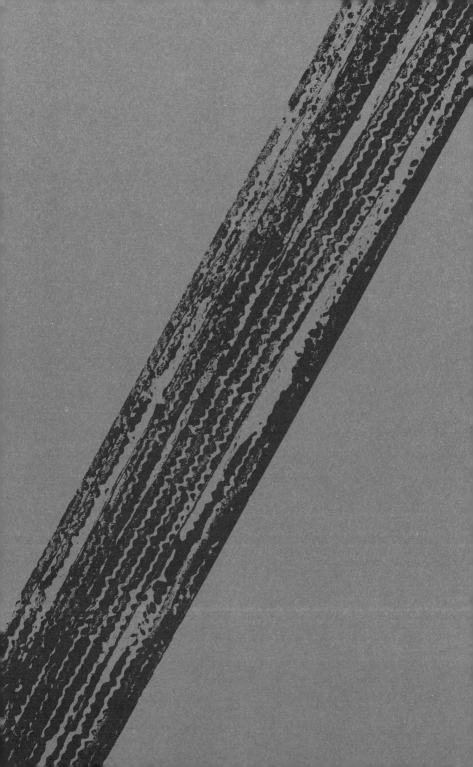

1

At The Derby

Bang! Crash! The old green Buick backed into the front of the red Ford. S-s-s-s-s-s-s-s! Now the Ford had a broken radiator.

"He got him! He got him!" called Tap. "The green Buick is the only car that can run now."

"Boy, that was good," said Woody. "I am glad you had me come with you, Tap. I didn't know a destruction derby was so much fun. And the big Derby is still to come."

"Let's go down and get something to eat," said Tap. "They have to take the cars off the track before the big Derby."

While the boys were eating, Tap said, "Do you think you will like the work Mr. Carter got for you to do while school is out? He liked your work in shop."

"I think I will like the work," said Woody. "You know how much I like cars."

5

Woody said, "Working in a gas station, I can work with cars all day. The money will be good, too. Tap, I want to fix my hot rod up. The Bumble Bee would make a good drag race car. It would take about $300.00, I think."

"It would be fun to have a good drag car and be in drag races," said Tap. "Maybe we can think of some way for you to get $300.00 to fix up the Bumble Bee. Let's go back now. The big Destruction Derby is going to start. We want to be there to see it."

Tap and Woody were seeing their first Destruction Derby today. The first rounds of the Derby were over now. All of the cars that could run after the first rounds would now be in the big Derby. The cars were just coming out of the pits.

"They are banged up," said Tap.

"Yes, they are. They only use old cars that aren't much good," said Woody.

The cars lined up in front of the stands in two lines. Some of the cars faced the stands while some had their backs to the stands. The cars started to back out.

"Why do they back out every time?" said Tap.

"The drivers want to keep the front of their cars from being hit," said Woody. "If the radiator gets broken, the engine gets too hot and the car can't run. They try to run into the fenders on the other cars, too."

6

Woody went on, "If the fender cuts the tire, the car can't go fast. Other drivers can hit the radiator then."

R-r-r-r-r-r-rooooom! Every car was now backing up and trying to run into other cars. All of the drivers had a stick with a white flag fastened to it on the door of their cars. When the car could not run any more, the driver broke the stick off. Then the other drivers could not hit him. That car was out of the Derby.

Many of the cars had names and pictures painted on them. Some cars had the name of the driver or the people who owned the car painted on them, too.

Now a black Ford was trying to back into a white Chevy. The driver of the Ford wanted to run into the Chevy's radiator. While the Ford was backing up to get the Chevy, an old black Cadillac, named Old Money-bags, backed into the Ford. S-s-s-s-s-s-s-s went the Ford's radiator. Now the Ford could not go. It was out of the Derby.

Old Money-bags was backing up now and running into many cars. Old Money-bags was a big car and when it hit a car, that car was out of the Derby.

Tap said, "No car is going to stop Old Money-bags. That car will win the Destruction Derby. It has won many times."

"The other cars are not as big as that Cadillac," said Woody. "How I want to be in a Destruction Derby, Tap! I'd like to try to stop Old Money-bags. It looks like fun."

After a time the only cars running were Old Money-bags and a little red Ford, named Red-hot. Old Money-bags was after Red-hot. They went around and around. Old Money-bags was the biggest car, but it could not turn as fast as the little car. Red-hot was keeping out of Old Money-bag's way. The driver of the little car didn't want to be hit by the big car.

The people were all calling, "Go! Red-hot, go!" They wanted the little car to win.

Tap said, "Red-hot is too little. Old Money-bags will hurt the little Ford." Just then Old Money-bags tried to run into Red-hot. The big car bumped the little Ford but did not hurt it. Old Money-bags was going so fast it could not stop and ran into one of the cars that was out of the Derby. Old Money-bags got his fender caught on the fender of this car. The Cadillac went ahead and then back, ahead and then back, trying to get away.

The driver of Red-hot could see that Old Money-bags could not get away. Red-hot backed up. Now he was going fast. Bang! Red-hot had backed into the radiator of Old Money-bags. Could the little Ford hurt the big Cadillac?

Now the radiator on the Cadillac went s-s-s-s-s-s-s-s. It was broken. The big car could not run any more. Red-hot was the one to win.

The driver of Red-hot was up on the stand now in front of all of the people. A man said, "Red-hot wins the Destruction Derby and $300.00."

As they left in Woody's hot rod, Woody said, "Do they give $300.00 away every time there is a Destruction Derby?"

"Yes," said Tap. "Every time there is a Destruction Derby."

"I was just telling you about wanting to get $300.00 to fix my car and I find out that they give $300.00 away," said Woody. "If I could be in one of the Derbies and win, I would have the money to fix up the Bumble Bee and have fun, too."

"It would be fun to be in a Destruction Derby," said Tap. "But you don't have the right car for that. You wouldn't want to drive the Bumble Bee in one."

"No, I don't have a car to drive in a Destruction Derby," said Woody. "I'm not going to use Bumble Bee. This car will make a good drag car."

2

New Work For Woody

"Woody, pick up your things and then come eat," his mother called from the other room.

Woody picked up his clothes and other things and put them under the bed. He made the bed but left many bumps in it. All of his things that were around the room went under the bed, too, or into other places. Woody went out to eat.

"Thank you for picking up your things, Woody," said his mother. "You know how much I have to do before I go to work."

Woody looked at his mother. She did have to work hard. Now he was sorry that he had not put his things in the right places. Woody ran back into his room. He called, "I'll be right with you, Mother."

Woody pulled his clothes out from under the bed. He ran around putting them away.

11

Then Woody pulled the bed clothes back. This time he made the bed as well as he could.

Woody looked around his room, "What do you know?" he said. "It was not any harder to clean my room up the right way. Why have I been putting my things under the bed all this time?"

"Come on, Woody," called his mother. "You want to be on time your first day at work."

While Woody was eating, he said, "Mother, Tap and I went to a Destruction Derby. I would like to get a car and be in one."

"You could get hurt in a Derby, Woody," said his mother. "Don't they run cars into other cars or something?"

"Oh, Mother," said Woody. "Destruction Derbies are safe. They do many things to keep the drivers from getting hurt."

Woody drove the Bumble Bee to the station. When he got there, Mr. Kelly had Hank, who also worked there, tell Woody what to do. Woody had been in a gas station many times and had worked around the shop, so it was not hard for him to do the work.

Hank had Woody fill the cars with gas, see if they needed oil, clean off the windshields, fix tires, and do other work like this. Woody could do all of these things. He had to work fast as many cars came into the gas station. Woody was to keep the gas station clean, too.

Mr. Kelly watched Woody working for most of the morning. Then he said, "You are doing very well, Woody. Hank and I are going over to get something to eat. I think you can run the station alone while we are gone."

Woody thought, "Well, I must be doing all right if they are going to let me work here at the station alone."

Just then a car pulled into the station. Woody ran over to see what the driver wanted. It was Cathy Carl. She said, "I thought you would be working here today. Look! I'm driving. Mother let me drive the car today."

Woody said, "Good for you! I thought you could do it." Woody had been helping Cathy with her driving.

Cathy had her rabbit in the car with her. She had found this rabbit when it was very little and had named it J. Rabbit. The J. was for Jack. At first J. Rabbit didn't like people and would not eat anything. Now the rabbit liked Cathy and Woody and would eat carrots and slices of apple right from their hands. J. Rabbit liked to drive in the car with Cathy and went every place with her. When he was in the car, he liked to stand up on the front seat and put his front feet on the door so he could see where he was going.

"Do you think J. Rabbit likes your driving?" asked Woody.

"Oh, yes," said Cathy. "He thinks I'm a good driver. I haven't run into anything. But this is the first time I have had the car alone."

As Cathy and Woody talked, they did not see a car pull into the station and wait to get gas. At last the man started his car and left. As he left, he called, "If you are going to stand there and talk all day, I'll go some other place to get my gas."

Woody looked up and saw Mr. Kelly and Hank coming back from eating. Mr. Kelly saw the man drive away and looked angry.

"Oh! Oh!" said Woody. "It looks like I have done it again. Go now, Cathy."

Cathy thought that Mr. Kelly would be angry with her, too. She started up the car. She was in a hurry, and this was the first time she had had the car out alone. She didn't go ahead. She went back. The car backed into a big pile of oil cans. Bang! Bang! Now there were oil cans all over the gas station.

Mr. Kelly said, "Look out! Look out! Now look what you have done."

Now the car went ahead, and Cathy left in a hurry.

Mr. Kelly said to Woody. "Look what you have done. You were just standing around talking. You're not waiting on the people. You can't work here anymore. You really don't do the good work that Mr. Carter said you would do."

Hank came up to Mr. Kelly and said, "Don't make Woody go, Mr. Kelly. I think he will do good work. He knows about cars, too. Just look at the work he's done on his hot rod."

"Well, all right," said Mr. Kelly. "I'll give you one more try, Woody. But you are here to work, not to stand around talking."

"Thank you, Mr. Kelly," said Woody. "I'm sorry." He could not say anything more. Hank helped Woody pick up the oil cans and pile them up again.

When Mr. Kelly had left, Woody said, "Thank you, Hank, for standing up for me. I want the work, and I'll work hard."

"I know you will, Woody," said Hank. "But no more standing around talking when there are cars waiting for gas."

Just then a hot rod drove into the station. Woody ran to wait on it. He was going to do good work from now on.

When Woody went up to the hot rod, he could see that the driver was Buck Brown. Buck said, "Well, look who is working here. It is the boy who likes to clean up. Well, let's see you clean up. Here is $.50 for gas and clean off my windshield."

Woody put the gas in the car and cleaned off Buck's windshield. Buck said, "Woody, clean that windshield off again. There is something on it. I can't see."

Woody cleaned the windshield again. Buck said, "That windshield is not clean. You are not doing good work, Woody. I'll have to tell Mr. Kelly. Now clean that windshield off again."

Woody cleaned Buck's windshield off again. He didn't want Buck to tell Mr. Kelly that he was not doing good work. Buck said, "That is not good enough. I'll talk to Mr. Kelly."

Hank was watching. He said, "That windshield is clean, Buck. I'll talk to Mr. Kelly, too if you don't stop giving Woody a bad time."

"Oh, I'm only having fun with Woody," said Buck. Then Buck said to Woody, "I'll fix you with Mr. Kelly."

As Buck drove off, Woody thought, "Not one thing has gone right today. Buck would turn up. I didn't want to see him. Now he is going to tell Mr. Kelly that I'm not doing good work."

Woody worked hard all day long. Some of his work was to clean up the station after work. Woody didn't like this work very well, but he had done it while working in the shop.

Mr. Kelly watched Woody work. He said, "Maybe you do good work after all, Woody. The station has not looked cleaner."

Woody said, "Thank you, Mr. Kelly." Maybe Mr. Kelly would like his work after all. Maybe he could keep on working here.

Mr. Kelly said, "Keep the station open, Woody. I have to go and get a car."

Mr. Kelly came right back. He was pulling a trailer with a car on it. This car was a black Cadillac, and it did look banged up.

When Woody saw the car, he said, "I've seen that car before." He went over to look at it. Now Woody knew that this was the black Cadillac named Old Money-bags that was in the Destruction Derby.

Woody said, "Is that car yours, Mr. Kelly? I saw it in the Destruction Derby. This car did very well."

"Oh, did you see that?" said Mr. Kelly. "This is my car. It should have been the one to win the Destruction Derby. My driver didn't do very well. I am going to get a new driver. How about cleaning up the station so we can go home, Woody?"

Woody went on cleaning the station. He was afraid to talk any more to Mr. Kelly about the black Cadillac. But Woody was thinking, "What would Mr. Kelly do if I asked to drive Old Money-bags in a Destruction Derby?"

3

The New Derby Driver

"Mother, I'm going to ask Mr. Kelly today," said Woody as he came in to eat.

"Ask him what, Woody?" said his mother.

"I am going to ask if I can drive Old Moneybags in a Destruction Derby," said Woody. "He said that he was going to get a new driver. They give $300.00 for first place, and it would help me make a drag car out of the Bumble Bee."

"If you drove Mr. Kelly's car, he would get most of the money," said his mother.

"I know," said Woody. "But I would get something. Mr. Kelly gives the driver $100.00 if he wins. I'm going to ask Mr. Kelly today."

Woody had been working at the gas station for a week now. Mr. Kelly liked Woody's work. Every day Woody thought that he would ask Mr. Kelly if he could drive in the Derby.

"I've got to go now. I don't want to be late," said Woody as he ran out to his hot rod.

When there were not many cars in the station, Mr. Kelly called, "Woody, come and help me work on Old Money-bags."

As they worked, Woody thought, "I have got to ask Mr. Kelly now. I don't know when I can ask him again."

Woody said, "Mr. Kelly, I'd like to ask you something, if you have a minute."

"Here comes a car, Woody," said Mr. Kelly. "Go see what they want."

Woody ran to wait on the car. He filled it with gas. When he had done that, he came back to help Mr. Kelly. Mr. Kelly said, "What did you want to ask me about, Woody?"

"Mr. Kelly, can I drive your car in the Destruction Derby?" said Woody. It was out at last.

Mr. Kelly just went on working on the car. At last he said, "Where did you drive in a Destruction Derby before, Woody?"

"I haven't," said Woody.

"How many days have you been working here?" said Mr. Kelly.

"I've been working one week," said Woody.

"How old are you?" asked Mr. Kelly.

"I'm 17," said Woody.

Mr. Kelly did not look angry. Woody hoped he would say yes.

"Now look," said Mr. Kelly. "Driving in a Destruction Derby is not as easy as it looks. The good drivers have been driving for some time. You have only been working here for one week, Woody. I would have to know you for longer than that before I would let you drive my car."

"Maybe you're right," said Woody. "But I want to try driving in a Destruction Derby. It looks like fun."

Mr. Kelly went on, "I have a new driver. He tells me that he knows all about cars and has been driving in many Destruction Derbies. He can win for me."

"Who is your new driver?" asked Woody.

"Buck Brown," said Mr. Kelly.

"Buck Brown!" said Woody. "He doesn't know anything about cars. He is not much of a driver anyway. I don't think he has been in a Destruction Derby."

"Woody," said Mr. Kelly. "Telling me things like that about a good driver like Buck will not help you. You are just talking like that because Buck is my driver. He said that you would try to tell me bad things about him because his hot rod beat yours."

"He beat me?" said Woody. "I beat him!"

"Now, Woody," said Mr. Kelly. "Buck said that's what you'd say. If you want to keep on working here, stop trying to run down Buck."

"There's a car," said Mr. Kelly. "Clean up this station before you leave."

"Yes, Mr. Kelly," said Woody as he ran to wait on the car.

Woody worked hard all day. He cleaned up all the gas station. It was some time before he was through. Just as he was doing the last of the work, Tap came into the station.

"Can I drive home with you, Woody?" said Tap. "Are you through with your work?"

"Yes," said Woody. "What are you doing out so late?"

"I have been working in a little band with some of the boys from the school band," said Tap. "I want to be good when school starts." He pulled out his sticks and beat a bang-bang-bang on something. "Is that the car that was in the Destruction Derby the other day?"

"Yes," said Woody. "That's Mr. Kelly's car."

"Maybe Mr. Kelly would let you drive it in a Destruction Derby," said Tap. "Why don't you ask him?"

"I did," said Woody.

"Is he going to let you drive?" asked Tap.

"No!" said Woody. "Do you know who is going to drive it?"

"No," said Tap.

"Buck Brown," said Woody.

"Not Buck Brown, the boy you beat with your hot rod?" said Tap.

"That's the same one," said Woody. "Tap, I'm not going to give up. I'm going to find a way to be in a Destruction Derby."

"How are you going to do that?" said Tap.

"I don't know," said Woody.

4

Looking For A Car

"No, Tap," said Woody. "That Ford won't do. It's not a very strong car. I think I'll talk to Hank and see what car he thinks I should have for the Destruction Derby."

"Well, it was only $75.00 and that is all you have," said Tap.

This was Woody's day off. Woody, Tap, Cathy, and J. Rabbit were looking for an old car for Woody to use in the Destruction Derby. Woody had $75.00 now from his work in the gas station. He was going to try to get an old car, fix it up, and run it in the Derby.

Woody had been working hard at the gas station. Mr. Kelly and Hank liked his work. Every day Woody came in before it was time for him to go to work to help Hank work on cars. Hank knew all about cars. Woody knew more about cars now from helping Hank.

The day after this they all went out looking at old cars again.

"All I see are used car lots," said Cathy.

"When we get an old car, you can watch us work on it," said Tap. "J. Rabbit can help, too."

"Oh, good!" said Cathy.

"This is the last lot we will go to today," said Woody.

They all got out of the hot rod and went around looking at the cars. J. Rabbit hopped around, too. They didn't see anything that would do for a Destruction Derby car. Just as they were about to go, Cathy said, "What is that way over there?"

They got out of the Bumble Bee again and went over to the back of the lot. Away back in the lot was a brown and yellow 1956 Buick station wagon.

They all went around the old Buick and looked at it.

"Hmmmmmmmmmm!" said Woody.

"Hmmmmmmmmmmmmm!" said Tap.

"Hmmmmmmmmmmmmmmmm!"said Cathy.

A man came over to see if they wanted the car. He said to Woody, "Take the old Buick and drive it around if you want."

They got into the car and Woody drove it down the street. Woody said, "This is a good strong car. I think it'll do fine."

Woody said, "The paint job's not too good, and the fenders are banged up, but it's a good car. If they don't want more than $75.00 for it, I can get it."

When they got back, they asked the man how much he wanted for the car. He wanted $125.00 for it at first, but came down to $100.00. That was as little as he would take. Woody said that he would try to get another $25.00.

As Tap, Cathy, and Woody drove away in the Bumble Bee, Tap said, "Where are you going to get $25.00 more?"

"I don't know," said Woody. "I think I'll take you two home and go down and talk to Hank. He will be alone now."

When Woody went into the gas station, Hank said, "Did you come back to work?"

"No, Hank," said Woody. "I think I have found the right car for the Destruction Derby. Can you come and look at it after work?"

Woody helped Hank and after work they went down to look at the Buick station wagon. Hank went around looking at the car. At last he said, "You should get this one, Woody. A station wagon would be good in a Destruction Derby. How much is it?"

"It's $100.00," said Woody.

"That is not too much for this car," said Hank. "Do you have that much money?"

"I only have $75.00, Hank," said Woody.

"Here's $25.00. You can give me the money back next week," said Hank.

Woody went home with two cars. Hank drove the Buick for him. Tap came out to look at the Buick. "That should be a good car," he said. "Where can we work on it?"

"That is what I would like to know," said Woody. "Let's see if Mrs. Green will let us use that old barn out in back of her place. There's nothing in it."

The boys talked to Mrs. Green. She said that they could use the barn if they would clean it up.

The next morning the boys cleaned up the barn. Woody said, "I know what I am going to be when I'm out of school, Tap."

"I thought you wanted to work with cars?" said Tap.

"I do," said Woody. "But I think I'm going to be a cleaning man. That is what I do most of the time."

When the barn was all cleaned up, the boys put the brown and yellow Buick in it.

"Now what do we do to it?" asked Tap. "How do we get it ready for the Destruction Derby? It needs work."

"Hank is coming home with me after work today. He is going to look at the car and tell me what I should do to it," said Woody who was looking under the car.

"Oh, oh! I thought something was not right here," said Woody. "One of the steering arms is all banged up. It would be too bad if it broke. I'll have to get a used one and that will be hard to do."

"What will you call the car?" asked Tap who was looking at the car. "Most of the Destruction Derby cars have names and are painted up."

"Well, I've got a Bumble Bee," said Woody, coming out from under the car. "What's yellow and brown?"

"I know," said Tap. "A yellow jacket is yellow and brown. Let's call it Yellow Jacket."

"Right you are!" said Woody. "We'll call it Yellow Jacket. I can get Cathy Carl to paint the name and a yellow jacket on the car. But, where am I going to get a steering arm?"

5

Getting Ready

"Who do you think will win the Destruction Derby, Woody?" said Mr. Kelly one morning as he was working on Old Money-bags.

Woody was afraid that Mr. Kelly knew about Yellow Jacket. He didn't know what to say. At last he said, "When is the next Destruction Derby going to be, Mr. Kelly?"

"In two weeks," said Mr. Kelly.

Woody was afraid to tell Mr. Kelly that he was working on a car for the Derby, too. Hank and Tap came by every day after work. Hank was helping them fix up the car for the Destruction Derby. The car was running good, but they needed a new steering arm. They had taken all of the glass out of the car and had fastened the doors shut so they could not open. These things had to be done to keep the drivers safe in the Derby.

Hank had helped Woody cut the fenders off a little. This would help keep them from cutting the tires if a car ran into them in the Derby.

Woody and Tap had put in a seat belt for the driver and Woody had a helmet. He could not be in the Derby if he didn't have these things.

There was not as much to do to the car as Woody had thought there would be. They could not do anything to make the car stronger. The car was ready now but for the steering arm. Every time he could, Woody went places where they had old cars. But he could not find a steering arm from a 1956 Buick like the Yellow Jacket.

By the next week Woody could give Hank back the $25.00 and had put up the money so his car could be in the Derby. Finding the steering arm he needed was harder than Woody had thought.

While Woody was working one morning, Buck drove into the station. Buck had on racing clothes. When Woody ran over to see what he wanted, Buck said, "Come on, boy. Here is $.50 for gas, and clean this car up. Do something about my brakes, too. They are making a noise."

As Woody worked, he said, "Why do you have the racing clothes on, Buck? Are you going to drive in a race today?"

"Not today," said Buck. "But next Saturday I'm going to drive in the Destruction Derby. Someone may see me and want me to drive a race car. I would make a good driver."

When Woody had put gas in Buck's car, he said, "I put gas in your car, but it will take some time to fix your brakes. It will be about $20.00, Buck."

"I'll not give $20.00 to have my brakes fixed," said Buck. "I'll fix them."

It was almost time to shut the station now. Woody and Hank were the only ones there. As Woody cleaned up the station, he was telling Hank about how Buck was going to fix his brakes.

Hank said, "Buck doesn't know much about fixing a car. I hope he doesn't do something he will be sorry for."

"I hope not, too," said Woody. "Here comes Buck now. Maybe we will find out how he fixed them."

Buck drove into the station very fast. When he was near Hank and Woody, he put on his brakes. His car didn't stop. It went right on and ran into a wall in back of the station.

Bump! Bang! Things were all over. The front of Buck's car was broken in. Woody and Hank ran over to Buck's car. "Are you all right, Buck?" asked Hank.

"I think so," said Buck.

Woody and Hank helped Buck out of his car. "What did you do?" said Hank. "Why didn't your car stop?"

"I don't know," said Buck. "I put on my brakes. They didn't work. I just fixed my brakes so they would not make a noise, too."

"What did you do to your brakes?" asked Hank. "How did you fix them?"

"I put oil on them," said Buck. "They were making a noise when I used them."

"You did what!" said Woody.

"I put oil on my brakes," said Buck.

Hank was laughing so hard he could not talk. "Buck," he said at last. "You don't put oil on brakes. Your brakes needed to be fixed. It will take more money now to fix up your car than it would have taken to have your brakes fixed the right way."

"Don't tell Mr. Kelly what I did!" said Buck. "Maybe he won't let me drive Old Money-bags in the Derby."

"We won't tell," said Hank. "We'll just say that your brakes didn't work. But you'll have to fix that wall."

As the week went by, all of the people at the gas station got very excited. Mr. Kelly was excited because his car would be in the Destruction Derby. Buck came in many times a day to talk to Mr. Kelly and to tell about what a good driver he was.

Hank and Woody were excited because Woody was going to be in the Destruction Derby. They had looked every day but had not found a steering arm that they could use on the 1956 Buick.

Now it was Friday, the day before the Destruction Derby. All of them at the station had lots to do. Hank got off at 3:00 P.M. and went to take a last look for a steering arm.

Woody was alone in the station now. It was almost time to go home. He had to work in the morning but would get off at 12:00. "I'll get to see the Derby," said Woody. "But I'll not be in it if Hank doesn't find a steering arm today."

Someone drove into the station and called, "I have it! I have got it!"

Woody looked around and saw Hank. "Did you get the steering arm, Hank?" said Woody as he ran to the car.

"Yes," said Hank. "I have found one at last. I'll go to your home. You come as soon as you can. It may take all night to fix the car. I don't know if there is time, but we can try."

"I'll be right with you," said Woody as he ran to shut the station.

6

Woody Has To Work

This was Saturday morning, the day of the big Destruction Derby. Woody and Hank had worked all night. The steering arm was in, and the Yellow Jacket was ready to go.

When Woody got to the station that morning, he thought that he would be through at noon. There was a note tacked on the door from Mr. Kelly. It said, "Woody, you will have to work in the station all day alone. We are all out at the track."

Woody was very busy this morning. Many cars came into the station. Woody ran from car to car trying to wait on all of them. Woody was thinking, "How am I going to get to that Destruction Derby? If I don't get there, I'll not get my $25.00 back. I should just go out there, but that would not be right. What am I going to do?"

Tap came into the station. "Woody, I went by your place. Your mother said you were here," he said. "When will you be through? We should be out at the track now."

"I know that, Tap," said Woody, as he put oil into a car. "Everyone has gone to the Destruction Derby. Mr. Kelly left me here to run the station. I can't just go."

"Let me work here. I'll keep the station open," said Tap.

"I would if I could, Tap, but you haven't worked in a gas station before. It takes a while before you know everything to do," said Woody.

As Tap left, he said, "I'm going to go see someone, Woody. Maybe it will help."

"Who is he going to see?" Woody thought. Woody was too busy that morning to think about it any more.

Many more cars came into the station. When Woody ran over to one of them, he saw that it was Hank. "Boy, am I glad to see you, Hank," said Woody.

"What is this Tap tells me?" called Hank. "I didn't know that you were working. I thought you were out at the Derby."

"You must know it all then," said Woody. "Everyone is out at the Derby but me. I have to work here. Mr. Kelly said that I must keep the station open."

"There is time if I hurry," said Hank. "Don't go away. I'll be right back."

"I can't go anyplace," called Woody. "What are you going to do?"

"I'll tell you when I get back," called Hank as he drove off.

Woody said, "Now what is he going to do? Everyone is going away and saying they will be back. I hope it doesn't take long. It is almost 12:00. The Destruction Derby starts at 2:00."

Then a car drove into the gas station. Woody ran to see what this driver wanted.

Before Woody had time to think very much about where Hank had gone, he was back again. "I have had a talk with Mr. Kelly," he said. "I can take your place here. I talked to him about your car."

"Was he angry?" Woody asked.

"Well, at first he didn't look as if he liked it. But then he laughed and said that if you wanted to be in the Destruction Derby that bad, he wouldn't try to stop you," said Hank. "Oh, yes, he did say that you would get a bad beating from Buck in the Destruction Derby. Now get going."

"I'm going. I'm going. Thanks, Hank," said Woody as he ran to his car.

When Woody drove up to Cathy's home, she and J. Rabbit were waiting.

"Why are you so late?" said Cathy as she got into the car. J. Rabbit hopped up on the front seat and put his front feet on the top of the door.

"I'll tell you about it afterwhile," said Woody. "Let's go get Tap and the Yellow Jacket."

When they pulled up in front of Woody's home, Tap was waiting for them. "I knew Hank would fix things," called Tap. "I have the Yellow Jacket on the trailer ready to go."

"That's great," said Woody. "It won't take so long."

Hank had let the boys use a trailer to take the car to the Derby. They could not drive a Destruction Derby car on the street. Soon the trailer with the Yellow Jacket was in back of the Bumble Bee and they were off to the Destruction Derby.

"How much time do we have?" asked Cathy.

"It is 1 P.M. now," said Woody. "The first round of the Derby starts at 2:00 P.M."

7

Get Ready

As they drove to the track where the Destruction Derby was to be, Woody, Cathy, and Tap did not have too much to say.

At last Cathy asked, "Do you think you can do it, Woody? You have only seen one Destruction Derby."

"That is just what I was thinking about," said Woody.

"Me, too," said Tap.

"I get into things," said Woody. "Then I find out I don't know much about them. Mr. Kelly may be right. I may take a good beating from Buck or some of the other drivers."

"If you don't try it, you will never find out if you can do it," said Tap.

"You're right," said Woody. "But I wouldn't like to have the Yellow Jacket all banged up and not win. It's a good car."

"It will be all right, boys," said Cathy. "I just thought of something. J. Rabbit will bring us good luck. A rabbit's foot brings good luck. J. Rabbit has four of them."

"You're right," laughed Tap. "We'll just have to win with J. Rabbit. Here we are now."

When they got to the track, some of the cars were going out on the tracks for the first round of the Destruction Derby. There would be four rounds before the big Derby. Every one of these rounds would have twelve cars in it. All of the cars from these rounds that could run, would be in the big Derby. The one to win the big Derby would get $300.00.

Woody was to be in the third one of these first rounds. The drivers liked to be in round one or two so they would have time to work on their cars before the big Derby if they needed to. Woody was glad now that he was not in the first round. He needed the time to get his car off the trailer.

Woody found his place in the pits where he was to keep his car. As he and Tap were taking the car off the trailer, they heard a loud crack. The first round of the Destruction Derby had started.

The Yellow Jacket was soon ready for the third round in the Destruction Derby. The boys fastened a stick with a white flag on it to the car. Every car had to have one of these.

If the car could not run, the driver broke the stick off. Then he was out of the Derby. The other cars could not run into his car.

Cathy watched the boys. J. Rabbit watched from the Bumble Bee. He didn't want to hop around here. There were too many cars.

"I just hope one thing," said Woody.

"What is that?" said Tap.

"I hope I'm not in the round that Buck is in," said Woody. "It will be bad enough to be in the big Derby with him. I know he will try to get me."

"Buck knows that your hot rod beat his," said Cathy. "He wants to get back at you."

"I'm afraid that is it," said Woody.

"Well, the Yellow Jacket is all ready now," said Tap. "Let's go watch the Destruction Derby until it is your turn."

On the way to see the Derby, they went by the pit where Mr. Kelly and Buck had Old Money-bags.

Mr. Kelly said, "Woody, why didn't you tell me you had a Destruction Derby car?"

"I haven't had it very long," said Woody. "I was afraid you wouldn't like it if you knew I was going to be in the Destruction Derby. I just had to be in one of these, Mr. Kelly, and I need the money."

"Yellow Jacket is a good car," said Tap. "Old Money-bags is, too."

"Well, you won't win any money. Buck here is going to win in Old Money-bags," said Mr. Kelly. "He knows how to win."

"That's right, Woody," said Buck. "And you are the one I'm going to get first. I hope you will be in round three. That's the one I'm in."

"The Yellow Jacket will be in round three, too," said Cathy.

"Good!" said Buck. "That will be your first and last round, Woody. After I run into you about twelve times you will not get that so-called car of yours out of the pits for the big Derby. Then Buck saw J. Rabbit. "What is that thing?" he said.

"That is J. Rabbit. I have had him from the time he was very little," said Cathy. "He's going to bring us good luck today. He always brings us good luck."

"Good luck!" said Buck. "If that rabbit comes around me, I'll eat him. I like to eat rabbits."

J. Rabbit let his ears come down until they were over his face. He put his head under Cathy's arm.

"Now look what you have done," said Cathy. "J. Rabbit is afraid. How can you say you would eat him? Come on, boys, let's go see the Derby."

"Cathy, J. Rabbit doesn't know what Buck is saying," said Woody as they walked on. "How can he be afraid?"

"He knows all right," said Cathy. "He can tell when someone is saying something bad about him. I don't know how he does it. Maybe it is just the way they talk."

They only had time to watch one round of the Destruction Derby. Woody watched the cars and the drivers. He wanted to see how some drivers could run into other cars and not have their cars hurt. He thought about the way he would drive in the third round that was coming up next.

Now this round was over. Many of the cars had to be pulled off the track. They could not run. Many of them would not be fixed in time for the big Derby.

Woody, Tap, and Cathy ran back to the Yellow Jacket. Round three was coming up.

Woody drove to the gate where the cars for this round were waiting to go in. Cathy and Tap ran to get a seat so they could watch the Derby. Cathy was saying, "Come on J. Rabbit, bring Woody luck."

Tap said, "You can ask J. Rabbit for luck, Cathy, but Woody has his luck with him."

"How's that?" asked Cathy.

"Woody has worked hard and fixed up a good car. He is a good driver," said Tap. "That is his luck."

"You're right, Tap," said Cathy. "But I'm going to ask J. Rabbit to bring Woody luck."

8

Go!

The cars made two lines in front of the stand. One line of cars faced the stands. The other line of cars had their backs to the stands. As Woody waited for the bang that would start the Derby, he looked at the cars.

Bang! The cars went r-r-r-r-rooooom and backed up. Woody was trying to hit cars and keep other cars from running into the front of his car. Every driver wanted to keep his car from being hurt in the first rounds.

There was a blue Ford in back of Woody. Woody backed into the front fender of this car. Now the Ford's fender was turned down. It cut the tire, and the tire went flat. The blue Ford was out of the Derby. Then a black Pontiac was coming at Woody. He tried to get out of its way. He turned the Yellow Jacket. The black Pontiac only touched Woody's car.

Now Woody saw Buck in Old Money-bags coming at him. Buck was not looking at the other cars. He was looking only at Woody. Woody tried to keep out of Buck's way.

Someone ran into Buck's fender. Buck had to stop, so Woody got away from him. Then a green Chevy came backing up to hit Woody. Woody turned just in time. Before the green Chevy could get away, Woody went ahead and then backed up fast. The Yellow Jacket banged into the radiator of the green Chevy. S-s-s-s-s-s-s-s went the radiator. The driver of the car broke off the stick that had the white flag on it. He called to Woody, "You got me, all right. I'm out of the Derby."

Woody was sorry for the driver, but he knew that someone had to be out of the Derby.

Woody thought that driving in a Destruction Derby was fun. But he didn't like to have Buck in back of him trying to run into his car.

Oh! Oh! There was Buck again. He came backing up at Woody again trying to run into his radiator.

Woody got away just in time. He said, "I don't want Buck to hit me with Old Money-bags. That car is strong. I want to get through the first round so I can be in the big Derby."

Then Woody saw an old brown Oldsmobile in back of him. It had its fenders caught on another car.

Woody saw that he could put another car out of the Derby. Then there wouldn't be so many cars in the big Derby. Woody backed his car up fast. Bang! The brown Olds wouldn't be in any more Destruction Derbies today.

"This is fun," said Woody. "My car has not been hurt much. If I can just keep from getting my car banged up for a little longer." Woody tried to go ahead. He found that his fender was caught on the fender of the Olds.

"Oh, help!" said Woody. "I can't go." Then Woody saw that Buck was getting ready to back his car into the Yellow Jacket.

Woody made his car go ahead and then back, ahead and back. Just as Buck was about to hit him, the Yellow Jacket broke away from the brown Oldsmobile. Old Money-bags hit the Yellow Jacket. He didn't hit the radiator but got Woody's fender.

"How do you like that!" called Buck. "I'm going to hit you again. I'll hit your radiator."

Woody tried to drive away but his fender was turned down so it had cut his tire. Now his tire was flat. Woody broke off his stick with the white flag. He was through for this round. He didn't want his car to be hurt any more.

Buck drove ahead to get ready to hit Woody again. "Stop!" called Woody. "I'm out of the Derby."

"I'm going to fix you so you won't be in any more Destruction Derbies," said Buck.

As Buck was getting ready to hit Woody again, there was a gun shot. Bang! That was all of this round of the Derby.

A man ran out and said to Buck, "Stop all of the cars! Stop all of the cars! This round is over."

Some cars could drive to the pits. Most of the cars had to be pulled away. They fastened the front of the Yellow Jacket up and pulled it to the pits and left it.

Woody got out to see if the Yellow Jacket could be fixed. Buck went by and called, "That is all of the Destruction Derby for you, Woody. You can go home now."

Tap and Cathy came running up. "How bad is it, Woody?" said Tap. "Can if be fixed?"

Cathy said, "Bad J. Rabbit! Why didn't you bring Woody good luck?"

"It may not be too bad, Cathy," said Woody. "I think all it needs is to have this fender fixed and a new tire."

"But can you do the work before the big Derby?" asked Cathy.

"I don't know," said Woody. "We need more help. I haven't done too much work like this. If Hank were only here, he would know what to do. We don't have the right things to work with."

9

Where Is J. Rabbit?

Woody and Tap tried to take the cut tire off the Yellow Jacket. The fender had been turned in too much. The tire wouldn't come off.

"We are going to have to fix that fender first," said Woody. "I don't have anything to fix it with."

"I fixed you boys up good," said someone in back of them. The boys looked around. There was Buck. "You can't fix that," he said. "You won't get back in this Destruction Derby."

"What's wrong, boys?" said Mr. Kelly. He had come up with Buck.

"This fender is turned down and is cutting the tire, Mr. Kelly," said Woody. "We don't have the right things to fix it."

"Come on over to our pit, and we'll let you use some of our tools," said Mr. Kelly.

"Don't do it! Don't do it, Mr. Kelly!" said Buck. "I put him out of the Derby. Now, he'll get back in it."

"If you are the good driver you say you are, you'll win, Buck," said Mr. Kelly. "Come on over, boys."

The boys went with Mr. Kelly to get something to work with. Cathy and J. Rabbit were in back of the Bumble Bee. Buck did not see them. "I'll fix them," said Buck. "They won't get this car started again." He opened the hood of the car.

"Get away from that car, Buck!" said Cathy. She came up in back of Buck with J. Rabbit. "What are you doing to that car?"

"What! Who!" said Buck. "Where did you come from, Cathy? I didn't see you."

"Well, I saw you and I know what you said. Now get away from that car or I'll call someone. I'll tell them that you were trying to fix Woody's car so it wouldn't run."

"I'm not doing anything to Woody's car. I was just looking at it," said Buck.

"You were going to do something. Now get away from that car," said Cathy.

Buck shut the hood with a bang. "I'll get back at you, Cathy," he said.

"How will you do that?" said Cathy.

"There is going to be one rabbit gone from around here," said Buck.

54

"Don't you touch J. Rabbit," said Cathy. "Here comes Woody and Tap. If you don't go, I'll tell them."

"I'm going! I'm going!" said Buck as he left. "But I'll get that rabbit."

"Now we have the right things to work with," said Woody as they came back. "If only Hank were here to help."

"What's wrong with your car, Woody?" said someone in back of them.

"Hank!" said Tap, Cathy and Woody.

"Am I glad to see you, Hank!" said Woody. "How did you get away from the station?"

"I called up a man that used to work for Mr. Kelly," said Hank. "He's at the station now. I thought that you would need me here. What's wrong with the car, Woody?"

"I think it is only this fender and tire," said Woody. "We have to get this fender fixed."

"Yes, you do," said Hank. "Give me that. We don't have much time."

Hank started work on the fender. Hank, Woody, and Tap all worked hard, too. Cathy put J. Rabbit down so she could give them the tools. Bang! Clang! Wham! J. Rabbit didn't like the noise. He hopped away.

Cars were starting to go to the gate to line up for the big Derby.

"The fender is almost ready," said Hank. "Get that tire fixed, boys."

55

Woody and Tap worked faster than they had worked before. Now the tire was on.

Woody got into the car and put on his helmet and his seat belt. "I'll be seeing you," he called. The Yellow Jacket went r-r-r-r-r-r-rooooooom and was off to the gate.

"Come on!" said Tap. "Let's go to the stand to see the Derby."

"Wait until I get J. Rabbit," said Cathy. She looked around for J. Rabbit. She could not find him. He was not there. She looked in the Bumble Bee. He was not there.

"Where can that rabbit be?" said Tap.

"Look!" said Hank. "Look at the back seat of the Yellow Jacket!"

They all looked at the Yellow Jacket. It was just going through the gate to line up with the Destruction Derby cars. J. Rabbit was standing on the back seat with his feet on the door. Maybe he didn't like the noise that all of the cars were making. Now he hopped down in the car.

Cathy, Tap, and Hank ran for the stands. Cathy said, "Woody doesn't know that J. Rabbit is in the car. J. Rabbit will be afraid. Maybe he will hop out and get hurt."

Hank said, "He won't hop out, and he won't get hurt. That rabbit will be safe. Woody is driving the car, you know, Cathy. J. Rabbit will be safe with him."

"But Woody has a seat belt and a helmet, and J. Rabbit doesn't," said Cathy.

"I don't think they make seat belts and helmets for rabbits," said Tap. "Cathy, just think of all the good luck J. Rabbit will bring to Woody."

The three of them went up in the stand to get their seats and watch the Derby. The cars were all lined up for the big Destruction Derby now.

10

The Big Derby

Bang! The cars all went r-r-r-r-r-roooooom and started to back up. Woody tried to look every way. He was looking for cars to crash into and was trying to watch out for cars trying to smash him. Woody did not know that J. Rabbit was in the back of the car. He was too busy driving to see the rabbit.

Bang! One car ran into another car right by Woody. S-s-s-s-s-s-s-s went one broken radiator. That car was out of the Derby.

Now Woody saw a blue Oldsmobile in back of him. He could not hit the Oldsmobile's radiator, but he hit the front fender.

Then Woody saw Buck and Old Money-bags coming at him. Buck turned his car around and backed up trying to hit Woody's car. Woody turned the Yellow Jacket just in time. Buck only knocked some of the paint off.

Woody said, "I'm going to get away from Buck. I want to try to run into some other cars and not have Buck trying to hit me."

Woody worked around some cars to another place on the track. There he backed into a red Chevy and broke the car's radiator. One of the fenders on the Yellow Jacket was banged up when Woody ran into the red Chevy. Woody was afraid that he could not go now. He made his car go ahead. The fender didn't cut his tire. The Yellow Jacket was not out of the Derby.

Then there was Old Money-bags again trying to hit Woody. Buck had found Woody again. Woody got out of Buck's way this time. Before Buck could go ahead, a car ran into the door of Old Money-bags. Woody saw this and backed his car into the other door of Buck's car. Buck's car was not hurt much, but Buck was very angry. "I'll get you, Woody!" he said.

Oh! Oh! There came a brown Ford right at Woody. Woody turned the Yellow Jacket to the left just in time. The two cars bumped their front fenders but they were not hurt.

Woody looked around and saw that most of the cars could not go now. Only ten cars were in the Derby. They all banged up. Two cars had flat tires. Woody said, "If I can just keep going."

Wham! Crash! One car had backed into another car near Woody. Their fenders were caught now. The cars were trying to get away so they would not be out of the Derby. Woody saw that he could put two more cars out of the Derby. He went ahead and backed into the front fender of one car. The old Buick was so strong that the fender almost came off that car. It was out of the Derby. Then Woody went ahead again and backed into the radiator of the other car.

"Well," said Woody. "There are two more cars out of the Derby. There are eight, now."

Here came Buck again. He wanted to hit Woody while Woody was putting the two cars out of the Derby. Buck only hit one of Woody's back fenders.

Buck was backing up now, trying to hit Woody. Woody said, "As long as he is backing up, I can get away from him. I can go faster ahead than he can go backing up."

Woody ran into another car and put it out of the Derby. He saw two more cars that had run head-on into each other. Both of these cars could not start again.

"There are only four cars left now," said Woody.

Buck was trying to get Woody again. He didn't hit Woody but backed into a car that was out of the Derby.

Woody, working fast, backed into Buck. He hit Buck's front fender so hard, the fender almost came off.

There was another big noise. Two more cars were out of the Derby. "There are only Buck and me left," Woody said. "Can my luck last? I'll just try to keep out of Buck's way. Maybe he will do something wrong."

Old Money-bags was coming at Woody again. Buck didn't try to back up any more. He was too angry to think about hurting Woody's radiator. He only wanted to run into Woody. Buck's car was right in back of Woody's car.

"If he doesn't look out, the last two cars will be out of the Derby," said Woody. Then Woody had a thought. He knew that the back of the Yellow Jacket was very strong. He let Buck keep just in back of him as they went around the track. He didn't try to get away.

When Buck was right in back of Woody and they were going fast, Woody tried his plan. He put on his brakes hard.

Buck was right in back of Woody. He could not stop. The front of Old Money-bags ran into the back of the Yellow Jacket. Now the old Cadillac's radiator was going s-s-s-s-s-s-s. The front of Buck's car was all broken in. Woody's car was not hurt. He drove off.

The last car that could move would win. The one to win had to drive his car around so people could see that his car was running. Woody drove around the Destruction Derby track. Broken cars were all over. Everyone watched to see if any of the other cars could run.

All of the people yelled, "Woody Woods! Woody Woods wins the Destruction Derby!"

People came running to get Woody. He drove his car to the front of the track. There was a big stand there. Woody Woods went up on the stand. The people were standing up and shouting, "Woody Woods and the Yellow Jacket win the Derby!"

One man said, "Woody you are the one to win the Destruction Derby. I have $300.00 for you. You came out ahead because of your good driving and good luck. How did you get your good luck?"

Woody started to say, "I don't know." The people were all laughing and talking about something. Woody looked around.

Somebody yelled at Woody, "Look in the back seat of your car!"

Woody looked in the Yellow Jacket. He saw J. Rabbit in the back seat of his car. Woody said, "Well, my good luck came because I had four rabbit feet and a rabbit in the car with me."

Cathy Carl ran out on the track. Tap and Hank were right in back of her. She ran to the Yellow Jacket and was going to pick up J. Rabbit. "I'm so sorry, J. Rabbit," she said, "Were you afraid of all that noise? Come, I'll get you out of this car."

J. Rabbit hopped into the front seat of the car. He put his front feet up as if he were going to drive and looked around. He didn't look afraid. Cathy said, "You bad rabbit! I think you like Destruction Derbies."

One man said, "Bring the rabbit up here so everyone can see the good luck rabbit."

Cathy got J. Rabbit and went up to the stand with Tap and Hank. When the people saw the rabbit, they laughed some more.

J. Rabbit wanted to get down. When Cathy put him down, he hopped back down and got into the Yellow Jacket again. The people laughed some more.

Everyone came up to the stand to talk to Woody. Mr. Kelly came, too. He said, "Woody, I was wrong. You are a good Destruction Derby driver. You beat Buck. He got angry and didn't drive well. Would you like to drive a car for me in a Destruction Derby?"

"Thank you, Mr. Kelly," said Woody. "I would like to drive for you. I'm sorry Old Money-bags is all banged up."

"So am I," said Mr. Kelly. "But the Yellow Jacket is a stronger car in a Destruction Derby than my car. Will you let me have the Yellow Jacket for $250.00? You can drive it in some Destruction Derbies."

"I'll be glad to let you have it," said Woody. "It takes too much money for me to keep two cars. Then I can use the money to fix the Bumble Bee up so it will be a fast drag car."

"Bring the Yellow Jacket over to the pits, and I'll give you the money," said Mr. Kelly. They all walked to Yellow Jacket.

Woody, Cathy, Tap, Hank, and Mr. Kelly got into the Yellow Jacket to go to the pits. Cathy looked around. "Where is J. Rabbit?" she asked. "He was in the car."

They all looked every place in the car for J. Rabbit. He was gone.

"Where's J. Rabbit?" yelled Woody.

A little boy was standing by the car. He said, "That man over there has your rabbit. He said he was going to take it home for you."

"What man?" said Tap. "Where is he now?"

"He is running over there by the gate," said the little boy.

"It is Buck!" said Mr. Kelly.

"He has got J. Rabbit," said Cathy. "He will hurt him. Buck said that he would do something to J. Rabbit."

"We have got to get him," said Woody.

Away they went in the Yellow Jacket after Buck. They saw Buck run through the gate and into the pits.

Buck was somewhere in the pits now. He was in back of the cars so they could not see him. He ran in and out of the cars in the pits. Woody and the others got out of the Yellow Jacket and ran after him.

At last Buck ran into a place where there was no way for him to get away. They caught up with him.

Mr. Kelly said, "We know you have J. Rabbit, Buck. Give Cathy her rabbit."

Buck said, "What rabbit? I don't have your rabbit. Do I look like I had a rabbit?"

"What is that under your jacket?" asked Cathy. "You have something under there."

"There's nothing under my jacket but me," said Buck. "I eat too much."

Just then J. Rabbit put his head out of the front of Buck's jacket. Everyone had to laugh.

Cathy said, "There! You have him! You were going to hurt him! Maybe you were going to eat him!"

"Give the rabbit back, Buck," said Mr. Kelly. "You won't drive for me any more. You are not a very good driver, and you were going to hurt Cathy's rabbit."

"No, I wasn't," said Buck. "I was pretty angry at Cathy for a while, but I wasn't going to hurt J. Rabbit. I just wanted some good luck. I didn't have any good luck today."

"J. Rabbit won't bring you good luck if he doesn't like you," said Cathy. "You have to be good to him."

"Here is your rabbit then," said Buck, giving Cathy the rabbit.

"If Buck was not going to hurt J. Rabbit, let's not talk about it any more," said Tap.

"You're right, Tap," said Mr. Kelly. "Here's the money for the Yellow Jacket, Woody. Hank, could you take the Yellow Jacket on the trailer to the station for me? Will I see you at work Monday, Woody?"

"I'll be there," said Woody. "Thanks for your help, Mr. Kelly."

Woody, Tap, Cathy, and J. Rabbit started home in the Bumble Bee.

"I didn't like to let the Yellow Jacket go," said Woody. "But I can drive it now and then. I'm going to make a good drag race car out of the Bumble Bee now. Let's go have something to eat."

"I could eat a-a-a-a-a-—", said Tap.

"You can say you could eat anything as long as it is not rabbit," said Cathy.

"I could eat a dog, a hot dog, that is," said Tap.

They sat in the Bumble Bee, talking and eating hot dogs. That is, everyone had a hot dog but J. Rabbit. He had a carrot, some lettuce, and an apple, and he didn't stop eating until it was all gone.

Cathy said, "Here is to Woody Woods and his first Destruction Derby."

Tap said, "And here is to the one who helped him win."

"There were a lot of people who helped me win. You all did. I could not have done it alone. Which one are you talking about, Tap?" said Woody.

"Why, J. Rabbit," said Tap.

"Here is to J. Rabbit," said Woody, Tap, and Cathy. "May he bring more good luck."

The Destruction Derby

Cars used in a Destruction Derby are old cars or ones that are not very good. Cars may not be made stronger for a Derby.

These cars are not used in a Destruction Derby. They are not good cars for a Derby.

These things must be done to a car before
it can be in a Destruction Derby.
Doors must be fastened shut.

All glass must be out of the car.

Fenders can be cut back ½ foot so they will not cut the tires so much if someone runs into them.

How a Destruction Derby is Run

Every car must be in one round before the big Derby. Enough of these rounds are run so all of the cars can be in one. The cars that can be made to run after this first round, are then in the big Derby. The drivers and their helpers can try to fix the car up after the first round.

The start of a Derby is like this:

Most of the cars try to back into other cars. If a driver used the front of his car to run into other cars, his radiator would be broken. Then the car would get too hot and would not run. The drivers try to run into the fenders and radiators of the other derby cars.

When a car will not go, the driver breaks off his stick. He is then out of the Derby and the other cars can't hit his car. The drivers do not get out of their cars until the Derby is all over. The Derby is over when only one car is left running.

Acknowledgements

Kenneth Shields - Illustrator
Photography Unlimited—Photographer

Special thanks for help provided by:
   Larry Mendelsohn - President,
   Spectacular Promotions, Inc.
   Islip, New York

Hot Rod - Woody Woods wants more than anything to own a hot rod and enter it in the hot rod derby. Buck Brown and his friends have other plans for Woody.

Destruction Derby - Woody Woods needs some money so he can buy parts to make his hot rod even faster on the track. The $300.00 prize makes the Derby a "must" for Woody.

Drag Race - Woody's hot rod, the Bumble Bee, is fast, but not fast enough to beat Buck Brown in the Drag Races. With the help of a strange new friend, Woody makes his hot rod even faster. But is it?

The Stock Car Race - Woody's interest in cars leads him to Mr. House's racing shop, and a chance to work on real stock cars. Woody learns something from a pretty visitor, and gets his chance to race a stock car.

Road Race - Woody Woods, while driving a high powered Lotus in a road race, is in an accident. His hands badly burned and his leg broken, he says he will never drive again. He gets over much of his fear, but it is on the day of the big road race that he must make a big decision.

Indy 500 - The Indy 500 is the toughest test of car and driver. Few drivers who begin the race finish it. Woody Woods has something to prove to himself and to his friends: that a "road race" driver can win at Indianapolis.